. She said | to me : *What are the seven wonders of the world .. ?*
I said to her : *Johnnie Walker and—but who cares about the others anyhow .. ?*

A woman's as old as she looks, a man s as old as he feels — and a whisky's as old as it tastes. You are not long in doubt about the veteran age of Johnnie Walker whisky. First the fragrance of its bouquet tells you much. And then the unusually smooth flavour confirms your first favourable impression. Age in a whisky is a vital thing ! You've age *and* perfect blending in every bottle of

Johnnie Walker

By Appointment to   *His Majesty the King*

Born 1820 - still going strong

Dewar's
"White Label"

ISBN   0   9508484   3   3   (Hardback only)

© Copyright The 'Ole Bottleman

Text set in 7½ pt Helvetica Medium, printed by John Mackie Printer, 5 Derby Street, Burton upon Trent, Staffs.

A PAINFUL HISTORY.

OH, listen to this doleful song
   And let the Muse explain
The sorrows of a Burglar which
   His name is Harry Payne.

Equipped with tools professional
   A-burgling he did go
At dead of night to Holloway,
   As you should clearly know.

He entered Jerry Carter's house
   While Jerry was in bed ;
And then to prig his property
   He dexterously sped.

All sorts of rare and precious things
   He swept into a bag,
And much he chuckled as he gazed
   On such a pile of swag.

But, sad to say, while creeping out,
   With giddy joy amazed,
A whisky bottle on a shelf
Resistless longings raised.

He quaffed the potent Farintosh
   With such potations deep
That heedless of his well-won gains
   He soon fell fast asleep.

And when the sun rose beamingly,
   Earth's mysteries exploring,
A Bobby found him on the stairs
   Mellifluously snoring !

MORAL *by Sir Wilfrid Lawson :*
   Let ev'ry burgling gentleman
      And each accomplished thief
   Now take the pledge teetotal, or
      They'll surely come to grief.

Pub-Jugs

and other Advertising Jugs

with Price Guide

by

The 'Ole Bottleman

Book 1

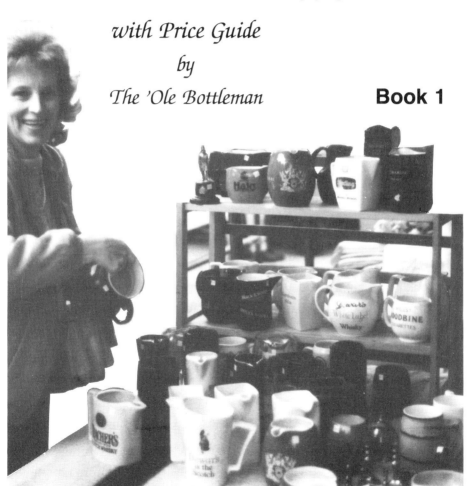

A Pub-Jug Collector inspecting a stall at a Hemel Hempstead old bottle market.

B.B.R. Publishing, 2 Strafford Avenue, Elsecar, Barnsley, S. Yorks. S74 8AA.

Acknowledgements

Keith Gratton, Jocelyn Lukins, Andrew Cunningham,

Alan Blakeman, Roy Morgan, Roger Dumbrell,

Robert and Marianne Macmillan, Eric Padfield,

Norman Lewis, Gerry Coran, D. Westcott,

Laurence Cooper, Neville Summers,

Daniel King, Harry and Mick Wiley,

Rob Green, Rob Goodacre, Ian and Rita Smythe,

Keith Wilson, Dave Ellison.

Louise Irvine, D. John Morton and Royal Doulton Ltd.

J. Johnston and David Barratt of George Wade & Son Ltd.

Mrs. S. Elson (Curator) and the Bass Museum.

From Collectors on all aspects of collecting covered in these Volumes.

We are particularly interested in photographing collections or receiving black and white photographs of groups of individual items for use in our future volumes.

Also we are interested in purchasing (or obtaining permission to copy) old advertisements related to Collecting in newspapers, magazines, books and trade catalogues etc., in particular:—

e.g. Black and White Magazine
      Patents Journal
      Doulton & Watts Co. Ltd.
      Price & Sons Ltd.
      Kellys Directory of Wines,
         Spirits & Brewing Trades
      London Illustrated News

      Trade Marks Journal
      The Mineral Water Trade Review
      Doulton & Co. Ltd.
      Maws Son & Thompson Co.
      Dairy Supply Co. Ltd.
      London Fire Appliances Co.
      The Pottery Gazette

Any additional information that readers are able to supply for future publications will be greatly appreciated.

Your Obediant Servants,
BBR Publishing

Contents

10.   Ales, Beers, Stouts

37.   Commemorative

42.   Doulton

65.   Miscellaneous

76.   Pubs, Hotels, Inns

85.   Soft Drinks

91.   Spirits

96.   Whiskies

Volume 2 will contain a full detailed index to the two volumes, together with details of jug manufacturers and how to date jugs.

Listings show "Firms" name in inverted commas for identification and in the brackets are the 'base' marks which usually refer to the pottery manufacturer, the 'firm' or 'company' itself, the selling agents, merchants or retailers.

PRICE GUIDE

The prices below are meant as a guide only and do generally show comparative values.

A . . . . £2 – £10

B . . . . £10 – £20

C . . . . £20+

D . . . . £30+

E . . . . £50+

Price by negotiation . . . . £xxx.

The above prices are for 'mint' items.

Main factors affecting the price are:–

Rarity ..... Condition ..... Age ..... Potter's Mark ..... Quality of Transfer ..... Detail of Relief.

I have quoted prices through this guide for "mint" specimens only – that is a jug in "as-new" condition. Chips, cracks, repairs, "smudged" transfers, faded or worn transfers, flaws in manufacture, scratches, stains, however slight – can reduced the price significantly.

It must be accepted that some of the very rare or older jugs will never be found in mint condition. But it can often be better to have a badly damaged rare or old jug which would probably cost less than a more common one, particularly if it "displays" well.

Cover Photograph

Top Row (L. to R.):–

1. Character jug of fox, (7″), "BEAM WHISKEY", (JOHN HUMPHRY'S POTTERY) (LTD. EDITION OF 2000), 1984 .... (C).

2. White jug (3″) with gold embossed lettering, "TEACHER'S", c. 1900 .... (B).

3. Grey stoneware jug with brown top and black transfer, (5″), (GROSVENOR POTTERY), c. late 19th century .... (D).

4. "WOOD'S OLD CHARLIE – FINEST JAMAICA RUM", (4″), (S. FIELDING & Co.), c. 1910 .... (C).

5. "WOOD'S OLD CHARLIE – FINEST JAMAICA RUM", (4″) with blue and red transfer, (FIELDINGS), c. 1910-20 .... (D).

6. Rectangular jug, (3½″), "WILLIAM YOUNGER & Co.'s. No. 3 SCOTCH ALE", (JAMES GREEN & NEPHEW Ltd., LONDON), c. 1920 .... (B).

7. Mr. Pickwick character jug, (4″), "PICK KWICK · DERBY · SELLS · JIM BEAM", (ROYAL DOULTON), 1983 .... (E).

Second Row (L. to R.):–

1. Figural of "Mayor", with bottle of "Worthington" beer held in his hand at the rear, (WADE), 1960's .... (C).

2. Blue willow pattern jug, (5½″), "JAMIE STUART, LIQUEUR SCOTCH", (J. & G. STUART Ltd.), c. 1920 .... (D).

3. White jug with hand-engraved green transfer, (8″), "JENNER & SONS" "SOUTH LONDON BREWERY" "1911 – CORONATION OF KING GEORGE AND QUEEN MARY", (ROYAL DOULTON) .... (£xxx).

4. Salt-glazed jug (8″) with brown top and black transfer, (DOULTON LAMBETH), c. late 19th century .... (£xxx).

5. Bass jug commemorating Coronation 1902, see rear cover.

Fron Row (L. to R.):–

1. Dark green square jug with red print, (4″), "JOULE'S STONE ALES", (WADE), c. 1960's .... (B).

2. White oval jug, (2½″), "OLD MULL FINEST SCOTCH WHISKY", (WEST HIGHLAND POTTERY – SCOTLAND), c. 1930 .... (A).

3. Pale blue jug with white embossed lettering (4″), "BODDINGTONS MANCHESTER", "BALLANTRAE WHISKY", (H.G. STEPHENSON, MANCHESTER), c. 1930 .... (B).

4. Sauce-boat shaped jug (2¾″ and 3½″), "OLD SCOTCH WHISKY, CRAWFORD'S", (WADE), c. 1970's .... (A).

5. Light green jug with blue lining, (4″), "GREENE KING FINE CAMBRIDGE ALES", (ROYAL DOULTON), c. 1920 .... (C).

6. "DEWAR'S WHISKY", (4½″), (ROYAL DOULTON), c. 1920 .... (C).

7. Yellow jug with black transfer, (5″), "FAMOUS WREKIN ALES", (JAMES KENT Ltd.), c. 1920 .... (D).

8. Orange jug with black transfer, (5″), "INDE COOPE & ALLSOP", (MINTON), c. 1930-40 .... (B).

Rear Cover Photograph

Two magnificent commemorative Pub-jugs:–

1. White jug, (8″), with blue hand-engraved transfer and red bottle label, "IN HAPPY COMMEMORATION OF CORONATION DAY JUNE 26th 1902", (SIR JOSEPH CAUSTON & SON Ltd.) .... (£xxx).

2. White jug, (8″), with blue hand-engraved transfer and red bottle label, "RECORD REIGN, DIAMOND JUBILEE, 1837-1897", (W. T. COPELAND AND SONS, STOKE-ON-TRENT) .... (£xxx).

Introduction

This is the first book devoted entirely to Pub-Jugs. These originated as 17th century serving jugs for ales in the inns and taverns of that period.

Some of the early jugs that were used were the salt-glazed bellamine jugs which were originally for wine. A development from these jugs were the English salt-glazed "Hunting Jugs" which were made during the 18th and 19th centuries, some of which are illustrated on page 10. These jugs were made in large numbers during the first part of the 19th century and by famous potteries such as Doulton, Fulham, Stiff etc. They usually have applied relief decoration of rural motifs such as trees, windmills, huntsmen, hounds, hares, foxes, men smoking and drinking, etc. Their form remained almost unchanged until the end of the 19th century.

During the latter part of the 18th century and the beginning of the 19th century jugs were made with the names of the inns and sometimes the innkeepers. They also began to advertise small breweries and brands of ales.

By the end of the nineteenth-century more and more advertising was appearing on those jugs which were now being used mostly as water-jugs on bar counters to add to spirits etc., breweries, distilleries, mineral water manufacturers, and all types of goods and trades connected with the "drinks" trade were being advertised on a wide variety of jugs made in pottery, glass, metal etc.

It was also during this period that general advertising jugs began to be made in large quantities for food, baby products, tobacco, medicine, shops, stores, companies and manufacturers, etc.

They have been made in large quantities this century and are still being made to-day in a large variety of colours and styles. In fact every pub has at least one on it's counter!

You can still purchase a Victorian advertising jug for a few pounds!

The hobby of collecting Pub-jugs has blossomed in the last four years and collectors have realized the large variety of contrasting shapes, colours, themes and subjects that are available. It is very easy to assemble an attractive display of modern Pub-jugs without spending much money. As these jugs are readily available for as little as £2 each, although it is possible to go into four figures for a very early piece. There are collectors of the "English" Pub-jug all over the world.

The older jugs are beginning to rise in price as more collectors join the hobby. This will mean that some of the older jugs will make good investments for the future.

These volumes will help to give the collector some idea of the wide variety of jugs that are available and also some of their comparative values.

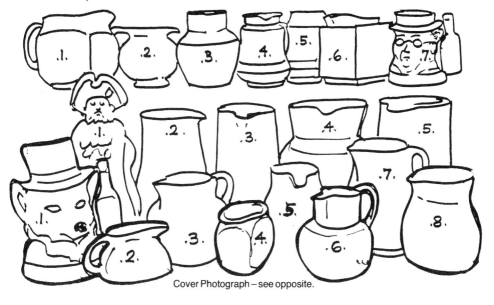

Cover Photograph – see opposite.

1

2

3

4

5

6

7

8

9

10

ALES
BEERS
STOUTS

Left: Brown salt-glazed ale jug (7″) "G & E FROGGATT, MAY 26 1928". (Nottingham type).
.... (£xxx)
Above: Two white Victorian jugs (6″). Left: Grey print of Wheatsheaf (Mocca type). Right: White relief panel on blue ground (Wedgewood style) .... (D).

Illustrations opposite:

1. 18th century slab sealed jug, the seal depicting Hogarths well known "Midnight Conversation". Fulham, circa 1780-90.
2. Sturdy jug of excellent quality; vines in relief around top, and hunting scene beneath, Mortlake, circa 1800.
3. Attractive jug, with village church and "harvest basket" in bold relief, possibly Lambeth, circa 1840-50.
4. Jug of fine quality with very attractive light brown metallic glaze. Impressed on the front, "R. Ellison, Burlington Arms, Keighley" and sprigged decoration in the form of a coaching scene. Brampton, circa 1830.
5. Small, good quality jug with impressed pattern to neck top and thumb grip to handle, possible Mortlake, circa 1830-40.
6. Very rare double slab sealed jug, with portrait of the Duke of Cumberland. Owners name and date incised in clay. Fulham, 1747.
7. Slender well proportioned jug with figures out shooting, Mortlake, circa 1780.
8. Cylindrical bodied jug by James Stiff & Sons of Lambeth, circa 1840-50.
9. Miniature jug with encircling band of flowers, including shamrock, rose, and thistle. Attribution difficult, circa 1850.
10. Greyhound handled jug with Bachanalian scenes, probably Chesterfield, circa 1840-50.

11

Top row (L. to R.): red jug (5″), with black/white transfer, "SHRIMP BRAND BEERS", (ASSOCIATED POTTERIES), c. 1920-30 .... (C); white jug (5″), black/red transfer, "EVERARD'S ON DRAUGHT, IN BOTTLE", (T. G. GREEN), c. 1920-30 .... (C); white jug with green 'lizard-skin' pattern and silver bands, "CHESTERS", "ALES & STOUTS", "WINES & SPIRITS" (SHELLEY), c. 1920 .... (C).

Bottom row: reverse side of jugs.

Opposite page, top row (L. to R.): White jug (5½″), with green bands, black lettering and red cross, "SALT'S BURTON ALES", (MINTON), c. 1900-10 ... (C); white jug (4½″), black and red print, "ROGER'S PRIZE MEDAL PALE ALES, BRISTOL", (MADE IN ENGLAND), c. 1930 ... (C); pink jug (4″), with black print, c. 1900-10.

Second row – reverse of top row.

Bottom row (L. to R.): White jug (4½″), with black print, "TENNANT'S ALE" – "WILEY'S WHISKY", c. 1910 ... (D); white jug (4½″), with black print, "WELL'S PRIZE BEERS WATFORD", (CLIFTON COTTLE), c. 1930's ... (B); white jug (3½″), with coloured print, "MANSFIELD ALES", c. 1930's .... (D).

See overleaf for detail of jug: top left on this page "SALTS BURTON ALES".

A traditional old green top and base pub-jug from a now extinct Burton-on-Trent Brewery, "Salt's Burton Ales" (C).

Glass jugs, top row (L. to R.): "ALTON'S DERBY ALE", c. 1900-20 ... (A); "ANGELO BAVARIAN BREWERY LIMITED, SHEPTON MALLET, ANGLO ALES", c. 1900 ... (B); "BRAEMAR SCOTCH WHISKY, ARCH, CAMPBELL, HOPE AND KING, GLASGOW", c. 1930's .... (B).

Bottom row (L. to R.): "EVERARDS BREWERY", c. 1960's ... (A); "PHIPPS NBC", c. 1960's .... (A).

Top row (L. to R.): White jug (4″), with black print and yellow medal, "CLINCH'S PRIZE MEDAL ALES, EAGLE BREWERY, WITNEY", (DUDSON BROS. HANLEY), c. 1937-8 ... (C); two-tone salt-glazed jug (3½″), "SOAMES, WELSH ALES", c. 1880 ... (C); pale yellow jug (3½″), "MAGEE MARSHALL & Co. Ltd., BOLTON, WIGAN & BURTON-ON-TRENT, (HANCOCK, CORFIELD & WELLER), c. 1920-39 .... (C).

Bottom row (L. to R.): white mug (3″), with red and black print, (GERMAN), c. 1880-90 ... (C); two-tone, brown top stoneware jug (4½″), "CHADWICK'S WELSH ALE, WREXHAM", c. 1900-14 ... (C); white jug with black print, "CORNBROOK, BARLEY STOUT", (WOOD & SONS, HOTEL WARE), c. 1950's .... (B).

Opposite page:
Top row (L. to R.): White jug (4½″), with green print, "BANK'S BOTTLED ALES, THE WOLVERHAMPTON AND DUDLEY BREWERIES LTD.", (E. CONEY & Co.), c. 1890-1910 ... (D); white jug (5½″), with blue bands and black print, "EADIE'S BURTON ALES", (T. G. GREEN & Co. Ltd.), c. 1900-14 ... (C); white jug (5″), with black print, "MANCHESTER BREWERY Co. Ltd.", c. 1900 .... (C).

Second row: reverse of top row.

Third row down (L. to R.): White jug (5″), with blue and red print, "CREESE'S ALES", c. 1920's ... (C); white jug (4½″), with red, black and brown print "SPECIAL CANNON IMPERIAL STOUT", (JOHN MADDOCK & Co. Ltd.), c. 1920's ... (D); white jug (6″), with blue and black print, "KEMP TOWN BREWERY", (HANCOCK, CORFIELD AND WELLER), c. 1930's .... (C).

Bottom row: reverse of row above.

White jug (3″), with black print, "MANCHESTER BREWERY COMPANY LIMITED", c. 1890 . (D).

White jug (5″) with green top and base "EADIES BURTON ALES" (probably Minton) c. 1920 . (B).

White jug (4½″) with green top "EADIES GLENEAGLES, OLD SCOTCH". (T.G. Green, Church Gresley) c. 1920 .... (A).

White jug (5″) with blue top "PETER WALKER & CO., ALES, BURTON-ON-TRENT" (Minton) c. 1920 .... (B).

White ash tray (3½″) "PETER WALKER & CO. LTD. WIENS & SPIRITS" (Minton) c. 1920 .... (B).

By courtesy of Bass Museum.

Left to right: White jug (3″) "WORTHINGTON" (Fieldings) c. 1930 .... (A).
White ashtray (2″) "ASK FOR WORTHINGTON IN BOTTLE" commemorating the Coronation in 1911. (Raphael Tuck) .... (B).
White jug (3½″) WORTHINGTON (T. G. GREEN & CO.) c. 1930 .... (A).

Victorian ale jug, white (9″), with fine hand-engraved transfer showing picture of the "BEEHIVE BREWERY, LIVERPOOL". (Coat of Arms for ELSMORE & FORSTER, CLAYHILLS POTTERY, TUNSTALL), c. 1860 .... (£xxx).
(J. POWELL was the owner during this period!)

Opposite page: Interesting jug (8″), white with similar hand-engraved black transfer showing the same premises but with "J. DAVIES" marked over the front entrance door, (no pottery), c. 1875 . £xxx. *The address was 54/8 Upper Beau Street, Liverpool).*

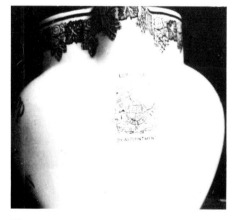

An attractive white jug (5″), black print with red hand trade mark "ALLSOPP, BURTON ALES" (Minton)
.... (A).

White jug (4½″), with black print, "FORGE INN", c. late 19th century .... (C).

IN BOTTLE

Opposite: An extremely rare part-print taken from an advertisement which shows an illustration of the bar in a public house specially erected in the Agricultural Hall, London for the Brewer's Exhibition of 1905/6 as the stand for Messrs. R. P. Culley & Co. Ltd.

Above a white jug 7″ high of the same period. It has a black and red transfer, "WORTHINGTON & Co. Ltd., INDIA PALE ALE, IN BOTTLE", (MINTONS), ... (C).
(A similar jug is shown in use in the illustration opposite).

Top row (L. to R.): Green top stoneware jug (4"), with black print, "LION BREWERY, GOLD MEDAL ALES ARE THE BEST", c. 1900-14 ... (B); brown top stoneware jug (4½"), "MATHEW BROWN'S FAMOUS STRONG ALE", (LOVATT), c. 1926 ... (B); two-tone salt-glazed jug (4½"), "SOAMES WELSH ALE", c. 1890 .... (C).

Middle row (L. to R.): brown top stoneware jug (4½"), "HARDY's GOLD MEDAL ALES & STOUT", (LOVATT), c. 1911; white jug (4"), with black print, "GREENALL'S ALES & STOUT", reverse "WHISKY", (BURLEIGH WARE), c. 1930's .... (C); blue top stoneware jug (4½"), with blue print, "PRAED'S", (PRICE), c. 1920 .... (B).

Bottom row (L. to R.): Dark yellow/brown jug (4"), with black print, "FLOWER'S PALE ALE", with picture of Shakespeare, (HANCOCK, CORFIELD & WELLER), c. 1904-14 ... (D); golden honey jug (4"), with black print, "ALL SAINT'S BREWERY Co. Ltd., LEICESTER", (HANCOCK, CORFIELD & WELLER), c. 1920 .... (C); bright orange jug (4"), with black print, "LUCAS, LEAMINGTON", (JAMES GREEN & NEPHEW), c. 1920's . (C).

TETLEY'S
PALE ALE.
EAST INDIA

Top row (L. to R.): buff coloured square jug, coloured transfer (6"), "STONES" (WADE), ... 1980's ... (A); buff coloured square jug, coloured transfer (6"), "STONES BEST BITTER" (WADE), 1980's ... (A); grey "CASTLE" jug, with black, white and red motif in circle (5¾"), "WEST COUNTRY BEERS", (WADE), ... 1970's ... (B).

Second row (L. to R.): dark brown jug with white lettering, (4"), "TENNENT'S LAGER", (WADE), ... 1970's ... (A); blue jug with white panel, (6"), "WORTHINGTON E", (WADE), ... 1980's ... (A); cream jug with brown transfer, (5"), "TOBY BITTER", (WADE), ... 1980's ... (A).

Above: Selection of jugs made by WADE pottery, c. 1960-70, price range .... (A-C).

Right: White jug (4½″), with coloured transfer, "JOULE'S ALES", picture of "DICK TURPIN" . (C).

Opposite, top: Framed card advertisement for "George's Bristol Beers" c. 1920, with below centre red jug (4″), with black print made for the same company, about the same period .... (C).

Opposite: (L. and R.): White jug (6″), with coloured print, "NALDER'S FAMOUS EMPIRE STOUT", "NALDER'S BROWN ALE, THE IDEAL" .... (D); white jug (5″), six-sided with black print, "ROGERS CHAMPION ALE", c. 1920-30 .... (D).

Above: White jug (6″), with blue print .... (D).

Right: White jug (7½″), with coloured print, c. late 19th century .... (D).

Above: For details of large jug see-overleaf. Small jug: Brown top stoneware jug (3″), "YE OLD MUSTY", "O'CONNOR", c. 1900 .... (B).

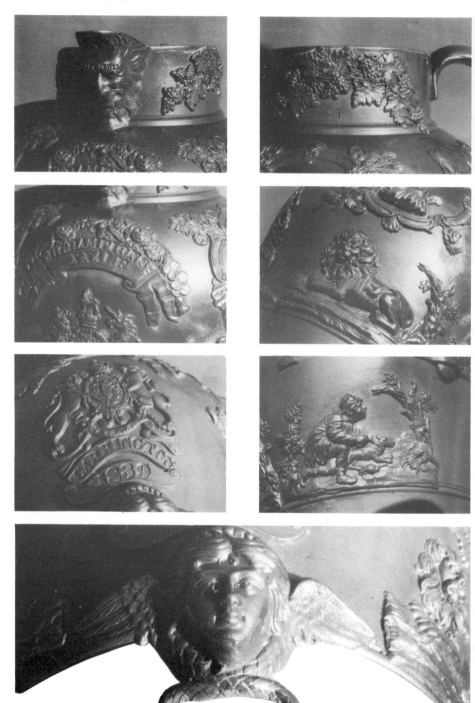

This unique, magnificent "Nottingham" pottery salt-glazed jug must be the ultimate in "Ale" Jugs.

Standing 15" high it is covered in very interesting subjects, in fine relief, all over the body.

Made during the 'reform' period it was probably made as a presentation piece to commemorate a special event in 1839.

Some of the features are (opposite page):–

1. Grotesque head with "JOHN BULL" incised on the forehead as the lip.

2. Finely detailed vine leaves and grapes around the neck.

3. On the shoulder on a scroll surmounted by a bird and two noses: "J. C. CHAMPIONS XX ALE".

4. Lions on either side of Royal Crest.

5. The Royal Crest of Queen Victoria, underneath on a scroll: "CARRINGTON 1839".

6. One of scenes depicting life in the country: A man with a dog who has just caught a rabbit. Other scenes include, cows, a bull, greyhounds and men drinking and smoking.

7. Cherub's head with wings either side, set under Royal Crest.

(Above):–

1. The Duchess of Kent set in an elaborate frame.

2. The Young Queen Victoria.

Both these portraits are very similar to those found on reform flasks of the period. . (£xxx)

Double sided "Nottingham" reform flask of same period.

33

Blue glazed jug (4½") "SAMUEL JOHNSON
L.L.D.", on the other side, "BARCLAY'S ALES
STOUT AND LAGER" (ASHTEAD POTTERY), bi-
centenary – 1984 .... (C).

There was a fine brew called Benskins
A very big hit with Redskins

Simply complete the limerick, fill in your name and address and hand in at the bar ~ it's that easy! You could win one of the exclusive Benskins Redskins pottery pint pots ABSOLUTELY FREE, and if you take a leaflet you could win, not only this exclusive pot, but a FREE PINT and a FREE HOLIDAY FOR TWO IN AMERICA THIS SPRING!

See local press for results

Assigning of copyright to Ind Coope Benskins Ltd for use wherever deemed appropriate is an express condition of this free entry competition.

Name
Address

FREE HOLIDAY FOR TWO IN AMERICA
PICK UP A LEAFLET FROM THE BAR AND GET
ON THE BENSKINS REDSKINS TRAIL NOW!

This colourful advertising mug was given away as a promotional prize in 1979. Details of the competition are shown on the beer mat illustrated .... (B).

35

Top row (L. to R.): Stoneware jug (6"), with brown top, and black print, "DRINK STENSON'S DRINKS", (PRICE, POWELL & Co.), c. 1906-14 ... (B); stoneware jug (6"), with blue top and black print, "CROWN LIQUEUR SCOTCH WHISKY", (LOVATT), c. 1910 ... (C); white jug with green top and black print, "MITCHELL'S AND BUTLERS DUMBARTON SCOTCH", (T. G. GREEN), c. 1920's .... (C).

Middle row (L. to R.): Stoneware jug (5"), with brown topf and black print, "EADY & DULLEY'S BITTER ALE", (PRICE, BRISTOL), c. 1890-1900 ... (C); white jug (5"), wit blue bands and black print, "MARSTON'S BURTON ALES", (T. G. GREEN & Co.), c. 1900-10 ... (D); stoneware jug (4½"), with brown top and black print, "ASK FOR BONNIE BRAE", (PRICE), c. 1896-1910 .... (C).

Bottom row (L. to R.): White jug (4½"), with red print, "FELINFOEL QUALITY ALES", (VELLUM ROYAL), c. 1960's ... (B); blue jug (3"), with black print, "ATKINSON'S ASTON ALES", (CAUSTON), c. 1920's ... (D); white jug (4½", with black print, "HULL BREWERY Co.", c. 1960's .... (A).

COMMEMORATIVE

White square jug (3") "OFFILERS ALES" commemorating the Coronation in 1911. (Fieldings)

A colourful blue top jug (5½") commemorating the Silver Jubilee of King George V and Queen Mary 1910-1935 produced for MANN CROSS MAN & PAULIN BREWERY (Wilkinson Bros. Elephant Pottery) .... (D).

Jug (3½") commemorating the Coronation in 1911, details of the back stamp are shown together with the detail of the other side .... (A). *(Matching ashtray shown on page 19).*

White jug (4") with blue band "MANN, CROSSMAN & PAULIN", "ALES & STOUTS", multi-coloured transfer. (SHORTER Bros., ELEPHANT POTTERY, S.E.1.), 1937 CORONATION .... (C)

White square jug (3") "OFFILERS ALES" commemorating the Coronation in 1911. (Fieldings) .... (C).

This Jug has been produced
in a Limited Edition to mark
the hundred Years that have passed
since Beer was first brewed at
The Cape Hill Brewery of
Mitchells & Butlers

Supplied by
Wade (PDM) Ltd
England

White jug with coloured print (5") "CENTENNARY 1879-1979." Details of back-stamp shown above .. (B).

39

Set of three white jugs with black transfers (2½", 3½", 4½") "HAILLWOODS MANCHESTER CREAMERY", celebrating Queen Victoria's Jubilee, ... (E). (*Purple and green prints are also known for these jugs*).

Both these white jugs with coloured prints were produced by WADE POTTERY, "TO CELEBRATE THE CORONOATION OF QUEEN ELIZABETH THE II, JUNE 2nd, 1985". The left-hand jug was produced for a number of breweries and distilleries. *(Other firms that used this jug were "MACPHERSON'S CLUNY WHISKY", "MELBOURNE BREWERY", "FAMOUS WREKIN ALES", "TRUMANS ALES", "SMITHS", "JAMES THOMPSON & Co. Ltd., BREWERS", "CATTERALL & SWARBICK'S", "WILSON'S", "C and S − XL − ALES").* The jug on the right was only produced for "NBC BEERS", − "A HEALTH TO HER MAJESTY". Both jugs ... (C).

DOULTON

Elaborate black transfer printed Whisky Water Jug commemorating the 100th Anniversary of the death of King George IVth specially commissioned from Royal Doulton, Burslem, by the Distillers of King George IVth Old Scotch Whisky, in 1930 .... (D).

DOULTON & CO., LIMITED, LAMBETH, LONDON, S.E.

DOULTON'S BROWN STONEWARE JUGS.

FIGURED AND PLAIN JUGS.

	Figured.	Plain.			Figured.	Plain.	
½-pt.	4s. 0d.	2s. 9d.	per dozen.				
¼-pt.	5s. 0d.	3s. 0d.	,,	3-pt.	17s. 6d.	9s. 0d.	per dozen.
1-pt.	8s. 0d.	4s. 6d.	,,	2-qt.	24s. 0d.	11s. 0d.	,,
1½-pt.	9s. 6d.	5s. 3d.	,,	3-qt.	36s. 0d.	14s. 6d.	,,
1-qt.	11s. 0d.	6s. 0d.	,,	1-gal.	48s. 0d.	18s. 6d.	,,

Jugs mounted in Metal can be had to order.

Also with NAMES, TRADE MARKS & BADGES IN RELIEF. Prices on application.

JUGS OF SPECIAL SHAPES

AND

WHISKEY FLAGONS.

Of various patterns in Salt-glazed Stoneware:

With or without Etchings of Premises, Trade-marks
or other Designs.

1 quart capacity. Prices from 8/- per dozen upwards.

Part cost of plate for printing from 5/6 upwards according to design

	POMPEII.		DORIC.		OXFORD.	
½-pt.	1-pt.		1-qt.	3-pt.		2-qt.
7s. 9d.	11s. 0d		15s. 6d.	22s. 0d.		29s. 9d. per doz.

These jugs are fine examples of Doulton transfer printed pottery. The transfers are hand-engraved in two colours black/blue.

Top left and right: white jug, (8½"), "BULL DOG BOTTLE BEERS", (Royal Doulton), c.1910, ... (F). *(There is also a "Doulton-Burslem" white jug which is 6½" high with the same transfer on).*

Centre – drawing taken from original design book of another variation advertising "BASS" and "GUINNESS".
(Illustration reproduced by permission of Royal Doulton Ltd.)

Right:– an extremely rare Australian white jug, (8½"), with blue transfer, "ASK FOR J. LADDS AERATED WATER & CORDIALS", (ROYAL DOULTON), c. 1916 .... (£xxx).

These advertising character jugs were specially commissioned from Royal Doulton by Pick Kwik Wines & Spirits of Derby.

Top Row: "Mr. Pickwick" with Jim Beam Bourbon bottle and "Mr. Pickwick" with Jim Beam Black Label Bourbon bottle, (both with light brown hat and dark brown coat) .... (B).

The miniature advertising bottles have 'open' bottoms (1985) .... (A).

Bottom Row: Limited edition jugs of 2,000 each made for promotion only: "Mr. Pickwick" with "Jim Beam Bourbon" bottle handle, ... 1985 ... (E); "Sergeant Buz Fuz" with "Dewars White Label Scotch Whisky" bottle handle, ... (1984) ... (E); "Mr. Pickwick" with "Whisky" and "Ale" bottle handle, ... (1983) ... (E).

A selection of Dewars green topped salt-glazed
jugs. Whisky jugs made by Doulton, 1880-1930,
price range .... (B-E).

ᗺewar's

"White Label"

The Whisky of Great Age.

A very interesting photograph from the 1920's of the interior of "The Black Watch Hotel", Aberfeldy, Perthshire, Scotland. The inset is of the water-jug on the bar counter. *(Photograph by courtesy of R. Macmillan).*

DOULTON

A selection of white jugs with black prints made by Royal Doulton, 1910-30 .... (C).

" *Does a man get wiser as he gets older?* "

" *Yes—as long as he gets YOUNGER!* "

WILLIAM YOUNGER'S 𝕾𝖈𝖔𝖙𝖈𝖍 𝕬𝖑𝖊

Green topped salt-glazed jugs with black prints by Doulton, late 19th century, 11″ and 2″ .... (E).

Two brown topped salt-glazed jugs (3″ and 5½″),
made for wine merchants, details from small jug,
price range .... (C-D).

Opposite page:

A selection three salt-glazed jugs, with attractive black decorative transfers:– top, blue topped jug (7½″),
"SPECIAL INVERCAULD SCOTCH WHISKY", (ROYAL DOULTON), c. 1910 ... £xxx; bottom left, brown
topped jug (7″), "EXCALIBUR SCOTCH & IRISH WHISKY", (DOULTON LAMBETH), c. late 19th century ...
£xxx; bottom right, brown topped jug, (8″), "GORDON & Co., IVY LEAF SCOTCH WHISKY", (DOULTON
LAMBETH), c. late 19th century .... £xxx.

Above a set of three kingsware jugs, "MEMORIES",
price range .... (C-D).

Right: Brown top salt-glazed jug (7½"), with black
print, "YOUNG & Co.'s ALES", c. 1900 .... (D).

Kingsware character jug (6½″), (ROYAL DOULTON), (1,000 – 1,500 made), c. 1910, ... (£xxx), (*A white version was also made by Royal Doulton). (Wade Pottery made a similar jug in two sizes*).

Top row (L. to R.):– Salt-glazed jug with brown top, (5¾"), "OLD MULL WHISKY", (ROYAL DOULTON), c. 1910, ... (D); salt-glazed jug, (8"), (DOULTON LAMBETH), c. 1920, ... (D); salt-glazed jug with brown top, (6½"), "POOLE & ANDERSON'S OLD SCOTCH WHISKY", (DOULTON LAMBETH), c. late 19th century, ... (D).

Page opposite: Very rare item – salt-glazed jug (7") with brown bands, commemorating Queen Victoria's Jubilee, but made for pottery retailer – "GIBSON & HOWSON & HOWORTH", – "PRESTON", (DOULTON), ... (E). *(The top print is taken from the rear of the jug, behind the handle!).*

Right:– an elegant salt-glazed jug, (9"), with black transfer, "VERY OLD DUNIVA HIGHLAND WHISKY", (DOULTON LAMBETH), c. 1891-1900, ... (E). *(There is a similar jug but with a transfer variation).*

Above: Treacle-glazed jug (7½") with brown bands and black print, (ROYAL DOULTON), c. 1910-20
.... (D).

Five brown topped salt-glazed jugs, c. 1880-1910,
price range, ... (C-D).

Extremely rare salt-glazed jug (10″), with incised lettering and the Prince of Wales feathers in relief on the front, "FILL ME WITH BASS OR ALLSOPP'S ALES," "AND DRINK LONG LIFE TO THE PRINCE OF WALES" (DOULTON LAMBETH), c. 1869-77 . (£xxx)

Another version of this jug exists with different lettering: "FILL ME WITH BASS OR ALLSOPP'S ALES," "DRINK A HEALTH TO THE PRINCE OF WALES".

Hand-painted character jug (4″), of Santa Claus, "DEWAR'S", (JOHN HUMPHRY'S STAFFORDSHIRE POTTERY) commissioned in 1985 by Pick-Kwik Wines and Spirits of Derby with special permission from John Dewar and Sons Ltd. .... (C).

Top row (L. to R.):– Salt-glazed jug, (6"), "WHITBREAD, ALES STOUT IN BOTTLE", (ROYAL DOULTON), c. 1920, ... (C); salt-glazed jug (6") with brown top, "HAIG & HAIG, WHISKY", (STIFF & SONS, LONDON), c. 1890, ... (D); salt-glazed jug, (6"), with brown top, "HAIG & HAIG", "WHISKY", (DOULTON LAMBETH), c. late 19th century, ... (D).
Note the metal rim on this jug was provided by the pottery to protect the rim and lip, see Doulton Advertisement).

Bottom row:– Salt-glazed jug (4"), with blue top and black transfer, "WALKERS", (ROYAL DOULTON), c. 1900-20, ... (D); salt-glazed jug, (5") with blue top and black transfer, "COURAGE'S AITON PALE ALE" (ROYAL DOULTON), c. 1920, ... (C); salt-glazed jug, (7"), with blue top and black transfer, "DART BRAND, ALES & STOUT", (ROYAL DOULTON), c. 1910, ... (D).

Detail of bases to jugs on page 62: "WATNEY'S" and "REID'S".

Detail of base to Dewar's "Santa Claus" on page opposite.

Page 60: top row (L. to R.): coloured toby jug (7½"), of an Irishman with a cudgeal in one hand and a bottle in the other, "CORBETT'S IRISH WHISKEY", "BEARS THE 'VERITOR' GUARANTEE", (J. A. CAMPBELL & SON, BELFAST), c. 1910 .... (E): coloured character jug (6"), "O.V.H. SCOTCH WHISKY Wm. GREER & Co. Ltd., GLASGOW, (ASSOCIATED POTTERIES Co.), c. 1920-30 .... (D); white character jug (6½"), with gold edging to hat and black transfer, (WADE), c. 1970's .... (D).

Middle row (L. to R.): white jug, (7") with blue transfer and coloured 'beer bottle' label, "BASS & Co., PALE ALE", "COMMEMORATING CORONATION DAY 1902", (SIR JOSEPH CAUSTON & SONS Ltd.) .... (£xxx); salt-glazed jug (7½"), with brown top, "GORDON & Co.", (DOULTON), c. late 19th cent. .... (£xxx); white jug (7") with green transfer print, "R. H. JENNER & SONS, SOUTH LONDON BREWERY", "CORONATION 1911", (ROYAL DOULTON) .... (£xxx).

Bottom row (L. to R.): white jug (5½"), blue 'lizard skin' pattern, "WHITE HORSE WHISKY", (SHELLEY), c. 1920 .... (C); white square jug (4"), coloured transfer, "PADDY THE WHISKY OF QUALITY", (ARKLOW), c. 1950-60 .... (B); white square jug (3½"), "OFFILERS ALES", (FIELDINGS) .... (C).

Page 61, top row: white jug (5", with green transfer and coloured T. M., "TOBY ALE", "CHARRINGTONS", (ROYAL DOULTON), c. 1936 .... (C); white jug (3¼") with black transfer, "WILLIAM YOUNGER'S SCOTCH ALE" "GET YOUNGER EVERY DAY", (ROYAL DOULTON), c. 1930 .... (C); salt-glazed, blue top jug (5"), "CLAYMORE RARE OLD SCOTCH WHISKY", (ROYAL DOULTON), c. 1920-30 .... (D); bright green jug (3½") with 'raised' lettering, "WATNEY'S ALES", (ROYAL DOULTON), c. 1938 .... (C).

Second row: pale jug (6"), "McCALLUM'S WHISKY IS PERFECTION", (ROYAL DOULTON), c. 1935 .... (D); pink jug (6"), "McCALLUM'S WHISKY IS PERFECTION", (ROYAL DOULTON), c. 1935 .... (D); white jug (8"), with coloured trasfer, "BASS & CO., PALE ALE", (ROYAL DOULTON), c. 1900-10 .... (D); green jug (3½"), with 'raised' lttering, "REID'S STOUT", (ROYAL DOULTON), c. 1938 .... (C).

Third row: white jug with green top (5"), "SALT'S IN BOTTLE", (MINTON), c. 1910-20 .... (C); salt-glazed jug (7"), with brown top "WOOLF'S ALES", (DOULTON LAMBETH), c. late 19th cent. .... (D); salt-glazed jug (8") with brown top, "THORNE'S SCOTCH WHISKY", (DOULTON, LAMBETH), c. late 19th cent. .... (E); coloured toby jug (9"), "TOBY ALE", (ROYAL DOULTON), c. 1934 .... (E).

Bottom row: white jug (3"), with yellow transfer, "SANDERSON'S SCOTCH WHISKY", (MADE IN ENGLAND), c. 1920-30 .... (A); white jug (8½"), with coloured transfer, "LION", (SHAW, 14, 18, HIGH HOLBORN, LONDON, W.C.1.), c. 1920-30 .... (B); grey jug (3½") with brown top, "YE OLDE MISTY", "O'CONNOR", c. 1900 .... (B); blue jug (4") with black transfer, "MITCHELL'S & BUTLERS", "DUNBARTON SCOTCH WHISKY", (T. UPTON & SONS, Ltd., BIRMINGHAM), c. 1920-30 .... (C); salt-glazed jug (8"), with brown top, "DUNIVER SCOTCH WHISKY", (DOULTON), c. late 19th cent. .... (E).

Above: The other side of Col. Bogey Whisky shown top right on opposite page *(Photograph by courtesy of Jocelyn Lukins).*

Opposite page:–

Bottom four pictures are all of the same salt-glazed brown topped jug, (7″), "PURE LOCH KATRINE WATER", "BODEGA – LONDON, BIRMINGHAM, LIVERPOOL, MANCHESTER", with two different views of the Loch, (DOULTON LAMBETH), c. 1869-72 .... (E).

Above two jugs of similar design but for different companies (L. to R): "ROGANO SPECIAL WHISKY", (DOULTON LAMBETH), c. 1869-72, ... (E); "COL. BOGEY WHISKY", (DOULTON LAMBETH), c. 1891-190 .... (£xxx).

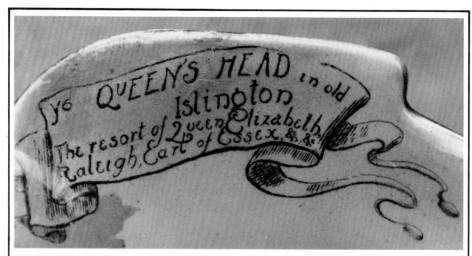

Top row (R. to L.): white jug (9″), detail of lettering inside lip as above, (ROYAL DOULTON, SERIES WARE), c. 1912, ... (E), (*there are two other versions of this jug, one with a blue print and the other fully coloured*); salt-glazed jug (6½″), "KINKORA IRISH WHISKY", (DOULTON LAMBETH), c. 1869-77, ... (D); white jug (9″), "SHEPHERD NEAM LTD", (ASSOCIATED POTTERIES), c. 1920-30, ... (C).

Bottom row (R. to L.): orange jug (4″), "ANSELLS, THE BEST BEER", (GREEN & CO., GRESLEY), c. 1930, ... (B); metal enamelled jug (4½″), c. 1920-30, ... (C), (*there is another version in yellow and brown*); yellow jug (5″), "TAKE A PEGG OF JOHN BEGG!", (CARLTON WARE), c. 1910-20, ... (C).

White jug (7″), with multi-coloured transfer "ESTABLISHED A CENTURY", "ANDREW W. COCKBURN", "DUKE ST., DAIRY", (K & B, Co.), c. 1910-20 .... (£xxx)

TESTIMONY FROM THE BRITISH ISLES

"Brought up from birth on the Allenburys' Foods"

All these are portraits of children
fed on the "Allenburys" Foods.

The remarks appearing underneath each picture are
extracts taken from the letters received with the
photographs.
The "Allenburys" Foods provide a complete dietary,
and children thrive upon them as on
no other diet.

Milk Food No. 1
From birth to 3 months.
Milk Food No. 2
From 3 to 6 months.
Malted Food No. 3
From 6 months.

Pamphlet,"Infant Feeding and
Management," sent free.

Allen & Hanburys Ltd.,
Lombard St., London.

The 'Allenburys' Foods

F240

Miscellaneous

THE " CREAM " JUG.

Decorated in various styles.

Capacity, about 1 quart .. **11/6**
      ,,   about 2 quarts .. **15/6**

DAIRY SUPPLY CO., LTD., MUSEUM ST., LONDON, W.C.1.

CREAM JUGS.

BROWN SALT-GLAZE STONEWARE.

Handled.

Size.	Per dozen.		Per gross.
Handled.	s.	d.	s. d.
Half-gill ..	2	6	
Gill ..	3	0	
Half-pint .	4	6	
Unhandled.	s.	d.	s. d.
Half-gill ..	2	4	
Gill ..	2	9	
Half-pint .	4	3	

BEST BROWN ENAMEL STONEWARE

Handled.

Size.	Per dozen.		Per gross.
Handled.	s.	d.	£ s. d.
Half-gill ..	2	10	
Gill ..	3	6	
Half-pint .	5	3	
Unhandled	s.	d.	£ s. d.
Half-gill ..	2	9	
Gill ..	3	6	
Half-pint .	5	0	

Above advertisement from 1930 showing cream jugs made to Dairies' requirements.

Opposite page: Interesting "baby food" advertisement with enamelled tin jug of same period shown above. Dark green jug (3″), with white lettering, c. 1910-20 .... (A).

White jug (4″) with blue transfer, "MILK RACE" (WADE), c. 1950-60 .... (B).

Hand-painted character jug (3″) containing tea-bags, "HARRODS" (Carlton ware), c. 1985 . (A).

Opposite: A selection of cigar/cigarette advertising jugs made by Wade Pottery, during the 1960-70's, price range .... (A).

White jug (6″), with black transfer advertising Q.A.N.T.A.S. the Australian airline, c. 1950's .... (B).

Interesting white advertising jug with black transfer made for a trader in Birmingham, c. late nineteenth century .... (E).

Above: White jug (4"), with green and yellow print, (WADE), c. 1957-8 .... (C).

Right: White rectangular jug, with green and yellow print, c. 1957-8 .... (C).
(Reginald Corfield Ltd., were the sole agens for Wade Pottery at this time).

Above: Extremely rare set of brown top salt-glazed, jugs with black print, made to advertise "JAMES STIFF & SONS" Pottery, c. 1980-90, ... (£xxx); another similar jug of the same period .... (D).

Above: Cobalt-blue jug (5″), with gold letters, (WADE), c. 1958,
.... (B). *(This is a promotional jug made for the Dunlop Rubber Co. Ltd.).*

Opposite page: top left, white jug (4½″), with light and dark blue transfer, "WILL'S CAPTSTAN CIGARETTES", (MADE IN ENGLAND), c. 1930 .... (A); top right, white stoneware jug (5½″), with blue top and blue transfer, "PLAYERS PLEASE", (LOVATTS LANGLEY WARE) c. 1930 .... (B); middle left, six-sided white jug (5″) with black/red transfer on each side, "PHILLIPS, EMPIRE PURE LEAF TOBACCO" "7½d. per oz.", c. 1920 .... (B); bottom left, white jug (4″) with black/yellow/orange transfer, "WILLS' GOLD FLAKE CIGARETTES", (MADE IN ENGLAND), c. 1930 .... (A); bottom right, white jug (5″) , with orange and red transfer, "WILLS STAR CIGARETTES", (MADE IN ENGLAND) c. 1930 .... (A).

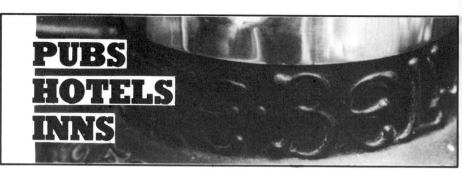

Interesting black jug (6¾"), with a 'matt' finish, in relief and silver top, "THE BELL EDMONTON", (Sands), c. 1895 .... (£xxx).

Top left, grey stoneware jug (7″), with brown top and black transfer, "WITH E. COLLINSON'S COMPLIMENTS, THE VICTORY, LOWER RICHMOND ROAD, PUTNEY", c. 1910 .... (B); top right, salt-glazed jug (4″), with brown top and black transfer, "SOUVENIR from YE OLDE KING'S HEAD, AYLESBURY", (Royal Doulton), c. 1910-20 .... (C); bottom left, white jug (5″), with blue/green banding and black transfer, " NEW INN", "LYDD", mocha ware type c. 1860-70 .... (D); bottom right, grey stoneware jug (8″), with brown top and black transfer "W. F. WILSON, PRINCE OF WALES, 339, BATTERSEA PARK ROAD, S.W.", (Price Bristol), c. 1920 .... (C).

Top: White jug with black transfer, "THE
COOPER'S ARMS", c. 1960's .... (B).
Above: White jug (3"), with blue bands and black
print, c. mid-19th century .... (C).

Right: White and beige jug (7"), with black print
"POMONA HOTEL", (SHEFFIELD), c. 1900 . (D).

Top row (L. to R.): White jug (4½"), with dark blue print, "F. CLAYTON, WHITE HORSE, TAMWORTH" with picture of hops, c. 1883-1902 ... (C); white jug (4½"), with sepia print and black lettering, "SOUTH DEVON INN, GAMLIN'S, DAWLISH", c. 1871-1893 ... (D); white jug (3"), blue top with black print, c. late 19th cent. .... (D).

Bottom row (L. to R.): Two-tone salt glazed tankard (5"), incised "G. INWOOD, SWAN INN, TWICKENHAM", c. 1850 ... (C); white jug (4½"), with brown print of barley sheaf, "S. GILES, MINER'S ARMS, STOCKINGFORD", (E. CONEY, BIRMINGHAM), late 19th cent. .... (C); white jug (4½") with black print and blue banding, "STOLEN FROM JOHN WHITTLE, EYE GREEN", c. 1847-70 .... (D).

Above: Brown hand-made jug (5"), very crude, "GREYHOUND BREWERY AND INN, SYLVIA-HENRY", c. 1980 .... (A).

White jug (6¼″, with black transfer "WHEATSHEAF, CHATHAM", (JAMES, GREENE & NEPHEW & SONS), c. 1920 .... (B)

This is a very good example of a Victorian pub-jug. White jug (4¾"), with sepia print and black lettering. Mr. Gamlin was the owner from 1871 until 1893 when he died.

White jug (2″), brown transfer, with red, blue and gold "on-glaze" transfer decoration, "BULL HOTEL, BURNLEY", (DUNN, BENNETT & Co., MANUFACTURERS, BURSLEM), c. late 19th century .... (C)

White jug (5″), with black print of "NEW STREET" and "THE NEW MUNICIPAL BUILDING" of "BIRMINGHAM", made for the "SHIP INN, PERSHORE", c. late 19th century .... (D).

Dote: 1897

C. T. MALING & SONS,

A and B FORD POTTERIES. NEWCASTLE-ON-TYNE.

FLINT GRINDERS BY THE OLD PROCESS.

Manufacturers of Every Description of SUPERIOR EARTHENWARE *for Home and Export Trades.*

GOVERNMENT STAMPED MEASURE JUGS & MUGS.

EXETER SHAPE
Printed only.
In quarts and pints.

In quarts, pints, and ½-pints.

PEAR SHAPE
In gallons, ½-gallons,
quarts, and pints.

Decorated in Moco (as shown on Pear Jug), also in solid Salmon, solid Blue, in Band and Line, Gilt, &c.

An interesting advertisement of 1897 showing standard jug shapes made for this period. This type of jug is found with advertisements for Breweries, Distilleries and Traders etc.

One of the common shapes for late 19th century jugs (6″), pale blue with black transfer, ... (C).

Schweppes
TONIC WATER
- does you Good

Top left, white jug with blue 'Willow pattern' print, "WHY NOT A SCHWEPLET, IT WILL IMPROVE YOUR WHISKY", (FIELDINGS), c. 1890-1900 .... (C); top right, yellow rectangular jug (3½", with black print, "SCHWEPPES SODA WATER", c. 1930 .... (B); right, white square jug (4½"), with red/brown transfer, "TAMPLIN'S TABLE WATERS", (MADE IN ENGLAND), c. 1930's .... (B)

Left: Grey stoneware jug (4″), brown top, "DUDDLES TABLE WATERS", (Price, Bristol), c. 1910 .... (A)

Buff stoneware (5½″), with light brown top, "PURNELL & Co., MINERAL WATERS, GUILDFORD", (Price, Bristol), c. 1920 .... (B)

Above: Grey stoneware (4″), with green top and black transfer, (WILLIAM PHILLIPS Ltd.), (Price, Bristol), c. 1920 .... (B)

Above: Grey stoneware jug (4″), with brown top and black transfer, "J. E. FITZGERALD, CAHIRCIVEEN", (Price), c. 1930 .... (A)

Left: Grey stoneware jug (4″), green top, "DUDDLES TABLE WATERS", (Price, Bristol), c. 1910 .... (A)

Art decor jug (4½″) with blue transfer, "ROSS'S",
"SPARKLING GRAPEFRUIT", "BELFAST TONIC
WATER", (GRAY'S POTTERY – HAND PAINTED),
c. 1930

WATER")

White jug (5″), with multi-coloured hand-painted on a black transfer, "COX, BOWERING & Co., Ltd.", "ARCADIA TABLE WATERS & FRUIT CRUSHES", (MADE IN ENGLAND), c. 1930 .... (D)

A soakin' wet day with the Bicester
Nearly killed Annabella, my sicester:
　　But her wheezins pneumonic
　　Were dispelled with Schweppes Tonic;
Now the 'stags' at hunt balls can't resicester.

Schweppes
TONIC WATER
- does you Good

SPIRITS

SEAGER'S
THE CHOICE OF CONNOISSEURS
SINCE 1803
The YEAR OF TRAFALGAR

GIN THE SPIRIT OF
TO-DAY

SEAGER, EVANS & CO LTD.,
THE DISTILLERY, LONDON.

White jug (3″) with blue print "SEAGERS GIN".
(Wilkinson, Royal Staffordshire Pottery) c. 1930's,
same date as advertisement above .... (A).

91

White jug (6½″) with blue banding and gold lustre and black transfer "COATES & Co., ORIGINAL PLYMOUTH, GIN" (WEDEKIND & Co., LONDON), c. 1900-20 .... (C)

White jug (4"), with blue and red print, ("MACDONALD SWAN & Co. Ltd."), c. 1950's
.... (B).

White jug with black transfer and gold bands, (3½"), "OLD CHARLIE FINEST JAMAICA RUM", (FIELDINGS), c. 1900 .... (D).

Selection of "GIN" jugs made by WADE pottery, 1960-70's .... (A).

PERTH

Four Crown Scotch Whisky

THE FINEST IN THE WORLD.

ROBERT BROWN LIMITED,

ROBERT BROWN LIMITED,

107 HOLM STREET, GLASGOW,

DISTILLERS,

BY ROYAL WARRANT OF APPOINTMENT, TO

HIS MAJESTY THE KING.

White jug (5″), with black print, c. 1910 .... (C).

Below: "BEAM BOOZER" collection of character jugs by JOHN HUMPHRY'S POTTERY, "ALY SLOPER", "MR. MICAWBER" and "TOBY FILLPOT", 1984 onwards .... (C). *(Limited edition of 1000 of each).*

White rectangular jug (4½"), with black transfer "JIM BEAM, BOURBON", (WADE), c. 1950 .... (A)

This rare card advertisement of the 1920's shows an orange water jug with black transfer, "KING GEROGE IV", OLD SCOTCH WHISKY .... (B). *(These jugs were usually made by SHELLEY POTTERY).*

A very decorative hand-made and hand-painted, 'Mary Gregory' style, cobalt-blue water jug with white enamelling (7½"). It has a clear glass handle and a broken pontil mark on base. "HAIGH'S GLENLEVEN OLD SCOTCH", c. 1860-70 .... (£xxx).

Top row (L. to R.): yellow jug with black and red lettering and coloured piper (6½"), "DEWAR'S IS THE SCOTCH", (WADE), ... 1970's ... (A); white jug with black and red transfer (5"), (WADE), ... 1960's ... (A); yellow jug with black and red transfer (6½"), (WADE), ... 1970's. Second row (L. to R.): yellow jug with black transfer (3¾"), (WADE), ... 1960's ... (B); dark green jug with red and white transfer (7"), (WADE), ... 1970's ... (B); dark green jug with gold, red and white label, (7"), ... 1980's ... (A).

Opposite a selection of jugs made by WADE, all with 'horse' motifs.

Top row (L. to R.): Dark blue jug (5½"), with white print, "WHITE HORSE WHISKY", (WADE), c. 1950's ... (A); Mid-blue jug (6½"), "WHITE HORSE SCOTCH WHISKY", (KIRKHAM POTTERY), c. 1960's .... (A); black jug (5¼"), with white lettering in yellow frame, "SCOT'S GREY BLENDED SCOTCH WHISKY", (WADE), c. 1970's .... (A).

Bottom row (L. to R.): Black jug (7"), with white and yellow print, "WHITE HORSE SCOTCH", (WADE), c. 1968-70 .... (B); brown jug (5¾"), with gold print, "GLEN ELGIN SCOTCH WHISKY", (WADE), c. 1970's .... (A); white jug (5¾"), with black, yellow and red print, "WHITE HORSE FINE OLD SCOTCH WHISKY", (WADE), c. 1908's .... (A).

Reverse of jug shown above.

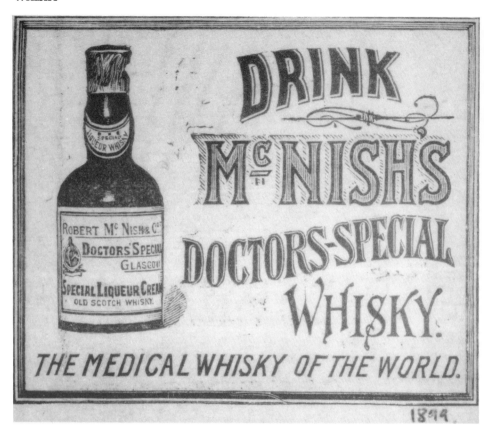

Above advertisement of 1899 for "Mc Nish's Doctor-Special Whisky".

DUNN BENNETT & CO LTD.
ROYAL VICTORIA POTTERY
BURSLEM
ENGLAND

Opposite page:— top,
left, six-sided white jug (3″) with coloured tartan "Mc NISH" (Dunn Bennett & Co. Ltd., as shown above) ... (B);
right, round white jug with coloured tartan "Mc NISH" (Dudson Bros. Hanley) ... (B).

A very interesting Victorian jug (8½"), pale blue with fine hand-engraved brown transfer and gilded edging, (DUNN, BENNETT & CO., BURSLEM), c. 1880 .... (£xxx). *A rare variation of this jug shows a spelling error:– "MEDCAL WHISKY".*

White jug with coloured transfer (5") "VAM-VAR WHISKY" (W.T. COPELAND & SONS), c. late nineteenth century .... (D).
(Opposite advertisement of same period).

Salt-glazed jug with blue top (5"), embossed on shoulder, "USHERS SCOTCH WHISKY", (Royal Doulton), c. 1920 .... (D).

Brown treacle glaze jug (7½"), with black print "WATSON'S BLUE BAND SCOTCH WHISKY, DUNDEE" (JAS WATSON & Co. DISTILLERS), c. 1890-1920 .... (D)

White jug with black transfer, (4″), "LION BLEND FINEST SCOTCH WHISKY" "H. WILSON & SON Ltd. SAVILLE ST., HULL", (NEWHALL POTTERY), c. 1900-10 .... (C).

There is quite a variety of these character jugs made by different potteries for distilleries and breweries. The original ones were made by the french pottery manufacturers Sarregulmines.

Top right:– fully coloured character jug, (5″), "HEATHER DEW, SCOTCH WHISKY", c. 1920-30 .... (D).

Top left and bottom right: fully coloured character jug, (6″), "O.V.H. 10 YEARS OLD WHISKY", (THE ASSOCIATED POTTERIES), c. 1910 .... (D).

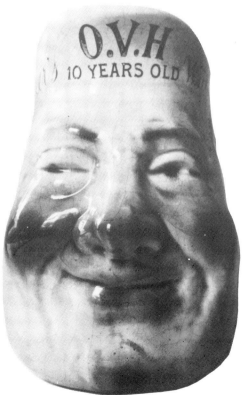

WHISKY

Top:– white jug, (3½″ and 6″), with black transfer, "TEACHER'S WHISKY", (FIELDING & Co.), c. 1920 . (B).

Bottom:– white jug (3½″ and 6″), coloured picture of boys playing cricket with whisky bottle as the stumps, "TEACHER'S WHISKY", c. 1910-20 .... (C).

Above: Brown treacle glaze jug (2¾"), with black print "WATSON'S BLUE BAND SCOTCH WHISKY, DUNDEE" (JAS WATSON & Co. DISTILLERS), c. 1890-1920 .... (D)

White jug with blue base and pal blue 'crazing' pattern. "WATSONS BLUE BAND", c. late nineteenth century .... (D).

110

Top: Rare white jug (5″), with green print, (SHELLEY), c. 1930, ... (E).

Below: Rare white jug (5″), with black print, (SHELLEY), c. 1920's, ... (D).

There are many variations in design for the Black and White scotch whisky jugs. These are a few. Right: white jug (5″), "BLACK & WHITE", "IT'S THE SCOTCH", (SHELLEY), c. 1925-40 .... (C).

Selection of black jugs (5″ to 7½″), with white transfers, all made by WADE POTTERY, c. 1950-70 .... (A).

Right-hand end, second row: black jug with white transfer, (5″), "BLACK BOTTLE SCOTCH WHISKY", (WADE), ... 1960's ... (B).

Page opposite: top (L. to. R.): 2 variations of similar white jug (4½″, 5″), with black transfers, "BLACK & WHITE", "SCOTCH WHISKY", (SHELLEY), c. 1925-40 .... (C); middle row (L. to R.): 2 variations of similar jug (4½″), "BLACK & WHITE", "SCOTCH WHISKY". (Top: WADE, bottom: HANCOCK, CORFIELD & WELLER) c. 1950-60 .... (A); white jug (4½″), with black transfer, "BUCHANAN'S BLACK & WHITE SCOTCH WHISKY", (SHELLEY), c. 1925-40 .... (B).

Above: A pair of white jugs (5″) with blue transfers made to commemorate "PRINCE CHARLE'S WEDDING", one for "PICKWICK SPECIAL ALE" and the other for "PICKWICK SCOTCH WHISKY" .... (B).

Left: Beige jug (3″), with sepia print, (JOHN HUMPHRY'S POTTERY) .... (A). *(A similar jug was also made for "PICKWICK SCOTCH WHISKY").*

Top row (L. to R.): White jug (6"), red orange banding with multi-coloured lancer, "COBBOLD'S LANCER WHISKY, IPSWICH", c. 1900-10 ... (D); white jug (4½"), with blue print, "ROBINSON BROTHERS, BOTTLED ALES", (S. FIELDING & Co.), c. 1900-10 ... (D); white jug (5½"), with green print, (REDFERN, HANLEY), "ELWORTHY'S PRE-WAR STRENGTH SCOTCH WHISKY, THREE CROWNS, CROWN BREWERY, KETTERING", c. 1920's .... (C).

Middle row (L. to R.): Brown top stoneware jug (6"), with black print, "ALEXANDER MELVIN & Co., BREWERY, EDINBURGH", c., 1890-1900 .... (C); brown top stoneware jug (5½"), with black print, "WILLIAM S. NEAL, WINE & SPIRIT MERCHANT, BELL BREWERY HOTEL", (PRICE), c. 1900 ... (C); white jug (7"), with black print, picture of monk riding a donkey, "LOWE, SON AND COBBOLD, STAMFORD, (CAUSTONS), c. 1920's .... (D).

Bottom row (L. to R.): Brown top stoneware jug (3½"), with black print, "MOORHOUSE, MINERAL WATERS, BURNLEY", c. 1900-10 ... (C); blue jug (3½"), with black print, "JAMES THOMPSON & Co. Ltd., BREWERS, BARROW IN FURNESS", (JAMES GREEN & NEPHEW), c. 1930 ... (C); Cream jug (3½"), with brown, red, yellow and black print, "MARSTON'S BURTON ALES", c. 1930 .... (C).

'Collecting Themes'

For collectors who like collecting 'themes', these three very attractive jugs show a contrasting selection of 'Hunting' signs.

Top: Yellow jug (″), with black print, c. 1930 ... (B); Bottom (L. to R.) – Green top stoneware jug (7½″), (PRICE), c. 1900 ... (E); White jug (7½″) with red and black print, c. 1920-30 .... (E).

The **DOULTON COLLECTOR**

A glossy bi-monthly magazine for Doulton Collectors, covering products both old and new, auction reports, articles by specialists on all aspects of collecting Doulton, bi-monthly price guide, new, views and events.

BBR PUBLISHING,
ELSECAR · BARNSLEY
ENGLAND · S74 8AA

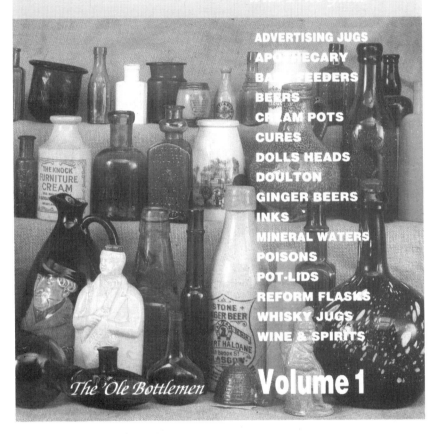

ANTIQUE BOTTLES COLLECTORS ENCYCLOPAEDIA

with Price Guide

ADVERTISING JUGS
APOTHECARY
BABY FEEDERS
BEERS
CREAM POTS
CURES
DOLLS HEADS
DOULTON
GINGER BEERS
INKS
MINERAL WATERS
POISONS
POT-LIDS
REFORM FLASKS
WHISKY JUGS
WINE & SPIRITS

The 'Ole Bottlemen

Volume 1

Collecting bottles and jugs is now firmly established as a major hobby in Britain as well as in the U.S.A. and Australia. This, the most comprehensive British book on the subject, provides collectors with all the information they seek.

This and following volumes will enable collectors, investors and dealers to identify, date and value their finds without the need for tedious research. The 'Ole Bottlemen are two of the U.K.'s leading international collectors and have collated and collected this information over a period of 10 years and have now made it available for all who are interested in the hobby.

These volumes cover all bottle collecting categories plus all types of associated jugs and flagons. Much of the information and many illustrations are published for the first time. The reference system is likely to become the acknowledged means of identification by collectors in Britain and overseas.

BBR PUBLISHING,
ELSECAR · BARNSLEY
ENGLAND · S74 8AA

SPECIAL PARAMEDICAL ISSUE
PLUS: BOTTLE AUCTION CATALOGUE (Subscribers only)

£1

British Bottle Review

THE WORLD'S LARGEST
SELLING BOTTLE MAGAZINE

HOW MUCH FOR ONIONS?

£1

LARGEST ISSUE EVER

British Bottle Review

THE WORLD'S LARGEST
SELLING BOTTLE MAGAZINE

INKS LINKS?

Also inside;

World's 1st valve hybrid 'Car Boot' bargains. New g.b discoveries. World's smallest onion? Willy's Wines—update B.B.R.'s 2nd auction CATALOGUE Plus massed of classifieds, etc.

GREAT BRITAIN   LINKS   AMERICA

THE SEA

WITH THIS ISSUE B.B.R. ENTERS ITS EIGHTH YEAR OF PUBLICATION

Number 28   Jan. Feb. March 1986

BBR PUBLISHING,
ELSECAR · BARNSLEY
ENGLAND · S74 8AA

WITH THIS ISSUE B.B.R. ENTERS ITS EIGHTH YEAR OF PUBLICATION

Kelth of London the well-known jug-collector and dealer with some of his enamel signs.

The large 18th century ale jug, bottom right is a detail of very rare "cut-out" enamel shown above which was used by the Stile and Winch Brewery Company for use outside their pubs (c. 1920).

ROBERTSON'S

THREE STARS
DUNDEE WHISKY

An exquisite old blended scotch whisky